C000088930

NORFOLK

Halswood

Published by Halswood Stationers

Copyright © Halswood Stationers
Copyright © on individual images resides with
the named photographers

All rights reserved. No part of this publication
may be reproduced, stored in a retrieval
system, or transmitted in any form or by any
means without the prior permission of the
copyright holder.

British Library Cataloguing-in-Publication Data
A CIP record for this title is available
from the British Library

ISBN 978 0 85717 005 7

HALSWOOD STATIONERS
Halsgrove House,
Ryelands Industrial Estate,
Bagley Road, Wellington, Somerset TA21 9PZ
Tel: 01823 653777   Fax: 01823 216796
email: sales@halsgrove.com

Part of the Halsgrove group of companies
Information on all Halsgrove titles is available at:
www.halsgrove.com

Printed and bound in China by (010)
Toppan Leefung Printing Ltd

Front cover: Thurne Mill. **Daniel Tink**

Back cover: Harvest at dawn. **Chris Herring**

Title page: Ranworth Broad. **Daniel Tink**

Right: St Benet's Level wind pump near Thurne.
John Duckett

Overleaf: Barton Turf church. **Chris Herring**

YOUR ADDRESS BOOK

Since the invention of the camera in the mid nineteenth century, photographers have found inspiration in the Norfolk landscape. Today, with digital cameras so widely available, almost everyone has an opportunity to capture mementos of a favourite place, or a chance event. But not all of us have the skill, or patience, to wait for that single moment when all the conditions fall into place and the perfect image is captured.

Like many of us, the photographers whose work appears in this address book, have fallen for the beauty and variety of scenery that the county has to offer. From dramatic seascapes and sweeping Broadland vistas, to impressive townscapes and tiny hamlets, each has been able to find a scene or scenery to arrest their interest. However, their skills usually far surpass those of us who happily snap away in order to record a moment. Their photography comes at a price, often with years of training and experience in the best use of complex and expensive equipment, with early starts and endless hours waiting for the right moment, and above all with an artist's eye in knowing what will make a good photograph.

These photographers are part of a long tradition of those who have been inspired to capture the elusive qualities of light, atmosphere and character that make Norfolk so special. Their work has been selected to portray something of the variety and range of contemporary photography being created today. Each in their own distinctive way, captures the essence of the place. They have been chosen as they are among the best known in the county and most have their homes here. Information about each can be found at the end of this book.

Address books tend to be well used and have a long life. Along with important contact details, they keep track of the user's friends and acquaintances, tracing their lives over time and from place to place. And, if properly attended to, an address book eventually becomes a journal in itself, and an attractive and permanent keepsake.

Whether you have bought this book for your own use, or receive it as a gift, we hope this *Norfolk Address Book,* with its superb pictorial reminders of Norfolk, provides years of pleasure.

USEFUL ADDRESSES AND TELEPHONE NUMBERS

Wildfowl, Wells-next-the-Sea.
Daniel Tink

A

The pier at Cromer.
John Duckett

B

Morning mist, Caister St Edmund.
Daniel Tink

B

B

B

Thurne Mill.
Daniel Tink

C

Windfarm off Great Yarmouth.
Mike Page

C

C

C

A field of Norfolk lavender near Heacham.

John Duckett

D

The Forum, Norwich.
Daniel Tink

D

D

D

Coltishall from the air.
Mike Page

E

Evening light, Blickling Hall.
John Duckett

E

E

E

Bircham Windmill.
Mike Page

F

Sunset sky, Cromer pier.
John Duckett

F

F

F

Wells-next-the-Sea.

John Duckett

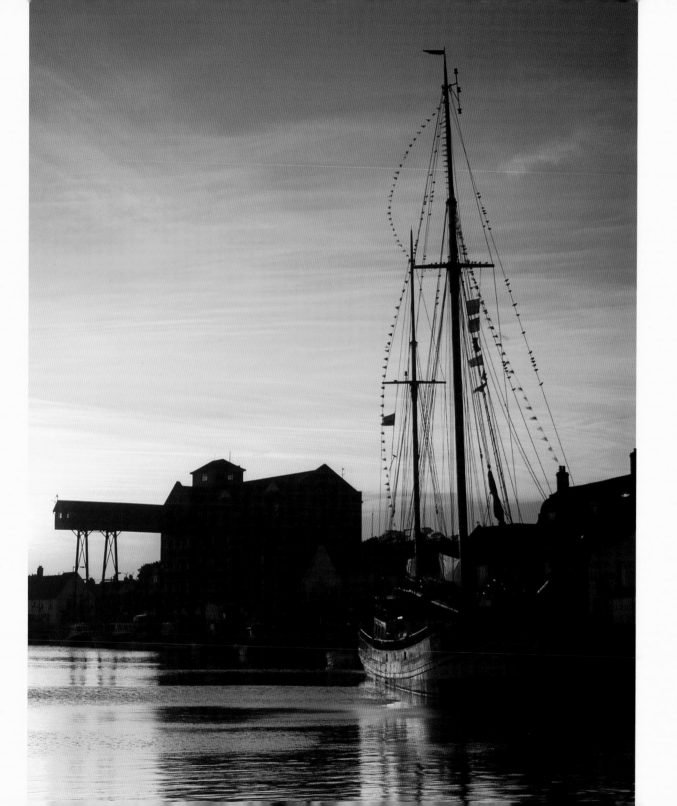

G

Malthouse Broad and Ranworth.
Mike Page

G

G

G

St Benet's Level wind pump, River Thurne.
John Duckett

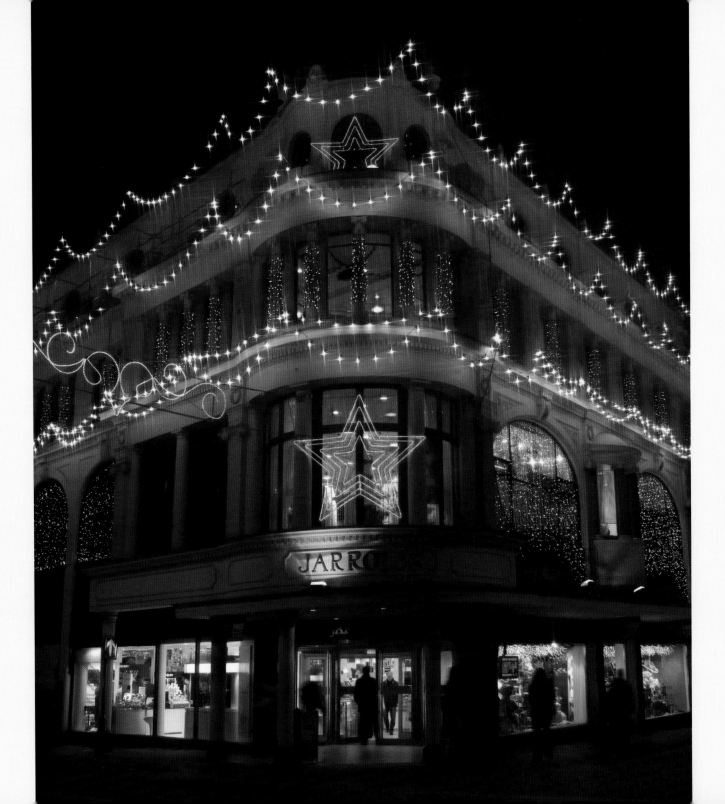

H

Jarrolds on London Street at Christmas.
Daniel Tink

H

H

H

Beach Huts, Well-next-the-Sea.
Daniel Tink

A November sunrise at Happisburgh.
John Duckett

I

Boathouse on the River Bure at Coltishall.
John Duckett

J

The Reedham Ferry.
Mike Page

J

Brancaster Staithe.
John Duckett

K

Fishing at West Somerton.
John Duckett

K

Castle Acre Priory.
Mike Page

L

Cromer morning.
John Duckett

L

L

L

Sutton Staithe.
Mike Page

M

Norwich Castle.
Daniel Tink

M

M

M

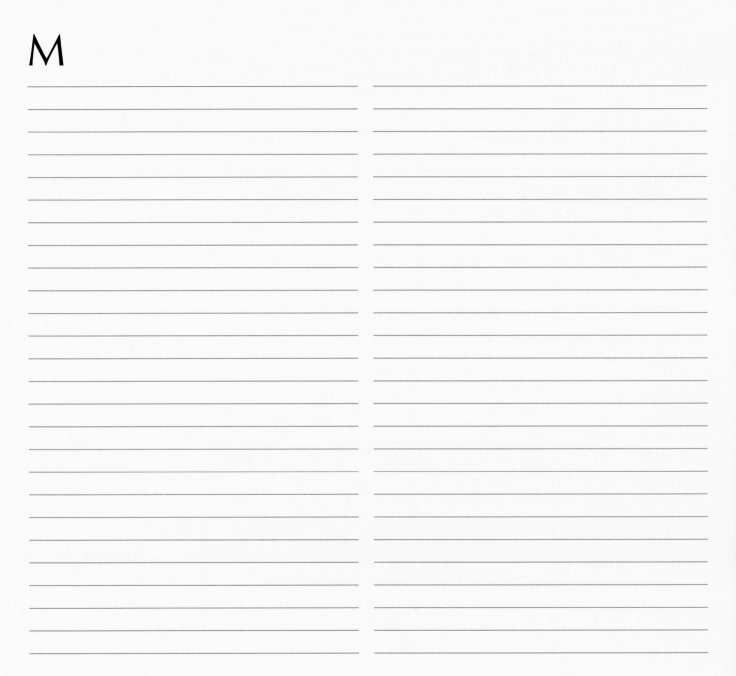

Wortwell Mill in winter.
Mike Page

Buxton Watermill on the River Bure.
John Duckett

N

At rest, Wells-next-the-Sea.
Chris Herring

O

Harvest at dawn.
Chris Herring

O

O

River Wensum and Fye Bridge, Norwich.
Daniel Tink

PQ

Barton Broad in December.
Mike Page

PQ

Wide Norfolk skies, near Cley.
John Duckett

Rockland Staithe on The Broads.
John Duckett

R

Denver Mill near Downham Market.
Mike Page

S

Norwich Cathedral.
Daniel Tink

S

S

S

Cromer Pier at Christmas.
Daniel Tink

Blakeney Point at high tide.
Mike Page

T

Coldham Hall near Brundall
Mike Page

Sunset on the cliffs at Hunstanton.
John Duckett

UV

Horsey Mill.
Mike Page

W

River Wensum taken from Fye Bridge.
Daniel Tink

W

W

View over Happisburgh.
Mike Page

Bramerton Woods End.
Mike Page

XYZ

XYZ

_____   _____
_____   _____
_____   _____
_____   _____
_____   _____
_____   _____
_____   _____

ABOUT THE PHOTOGRAPHERS

John Duckett is Norfolk born and bred. His photography focuses on capturing the unique skies and cloudscapes of this area, making best use of the more dramatic light found at dawn and dusk. His interest in photography began in his teens and he has developed his unique style through experience and experimentation with different camera settings and filters. For many years he worked in sales, covering the whole of Norfolk which stirred his passion for seeing how the light can completely change the atmosphere of a landscape. In recent years he has settled in north Norfolk and devotes more time and passion to his work as a photographer. He has published two books with Halsgrove _The Romantic Norfolk Coast_ and _Romantic Norfolk_ and has a third book forthcoming in 2010 based on his superb panoramic images of the county. Contact details: www.jduckettimages.co.uk.

Chris Herring first became interested in photography whilst studying the subject at college. Based in East Anglia, the Norfolk and Suffolk Broads and the coast are all only a short drive away and these are the areas he most enjoys photographing, as they provide many wonderful opportunities and locations often ignored by other landscape photographers. As a full time professional photographer he has undertaken a range of photography commissions for businesses locally and world-wide. He regularly has work published in local and national magazines, and contributes images and articles to a number of the UK's leading photography magazines. Forthcoming projects for 2010 include photographing wild birds on the North Norfolk coast, and photographing landscape images of Northumberland, Scotland, The Peak District, The Lake District, Jersey and the Welsh coast and countryside. Chris has two books forthcoming with Halsgrove _Norfolk -_ _A Winter's Tale, Panoramic Peak District, Spirit of Norfolk Windmills_ and _Spirit of Suffolk Windmills_. Contact details: www.theuklandscape.com. email: info@theuklandscape.com.

Mike Page, Gorleston-born, began his working life as a boat builder but in 1973 in partnership with his wife Gillian began a garage business at Strumpshaw, east of Norwich. Mike is now semi-retired and his son Martin runs the garage, which gives him more time to pursue his flying and photographic interests. He has a considerable library of aerial and wildlife prints which he makes readily available. In addition he supplies newspapers with newsworthy pictures and recently has produced aerial photographs for the _Eastern Daily Press_ in a series of supplements that have been very well received. His first book _A Broads-Eye View_ produced in partnership with Pauline Young and published by Halsgrove, was a huge success. This was followed by a veritable library of books based on his aerial photography, among them _Norfolk Coast from the Air, Suffolk Coast from the Air_, and _Norfolk from the Air_. Contact details: www.norfolkskyview.flyer.co.uk. email: mike@skyview.flyer.co.uk

Daniel Tink is one of the rising stars of photography in Norfolk. His collaboration with Stephen Browning in providing photographs for the book _Norwich_ played a significant part in the success of that book. Future collaborations with Stephen will include books on Norwich Cathedral and a book on Norfolk. Photography has been a large part of his life since 2003, while art, design and graphics have also long been major interests. He runs a successful website which acts as a showcase for his work, while also providing a photographic guide to Norfolk. Contact details: www.scenicnorfolk.co.uk. email:daniel@atutech.com.